# SCHOLASTIC
# Phonics

# Jess in a Mess

Published in the UK by Scholastic Education, 2021
Scholastic Distribution Centre, Bosworth Avenue, Tournament Fields, Warwick, CV34 6UQ
Scholastic Ireland, 89E Lagan Road, Dublin Industrial Estate, Glasnevin, Dublin, D11 HP5F

Printed by Ashford Colour Press
The book is made of materials from well-managed, FSC®-certified forests
and other controlled sources.

A CIP catalogue record for this book is available from the British Library.

ISBN 978-0702-30872-7

**Author**
Karra McFarlane
**Editorial team**
Rachel Morgan, Tracy Kewley, Liz Evans
**Design team**
Dipa Mistry, We Are Grace
**Illustrations**
Ellie O'Shea

# Help your child to read!

This book practises these letters and letter sounds.
Point and say the sounds with your child:

Your child may need help to read these common tricky words:

Before reading
- Look at the cover picture and read the title together. Read the back cover blurb aloud to your child.
- Ask your child: *Who do you think Jess is?* (the cat) *What might happen in this story?*

During reading
- If your child gets stuck on a word, remind them to sound it out and then blend the sounds to read the word: J-e-ss, Jess.
- If they are still stuck, show them how to read the word.
- Enjoy looking at the pictures together. Pause to talk about the story.

After reading
- Ask your child: *Why do you think Jack gave Jess a hug at the end of the story?*
- Talk about some of the good (and less good) things about having a pet.

Can you spot the squirrel on 6 pages?

3

Jack has a cat...

Jess, the cat.

Jack is in a huff.

The van is on
the zigzag box.

Jess tips the jug.

She tips the box.

The box hits the fan.

Jess is a mess!

Jack has the van.

Jack hugs Jess.

15

# Retell the story